5

JULIA DONALDSON · AXEL SCHEFFLER

By the creators of The Gruffalo

D0264777

e   An old lady complains her house is too small; a wise old man shows her it isn't.

6

JULIA DONALDSON · AXEL SCHEFFLER

Monkey Puzzle

By the creators of The Gruffalo

f   A witch gives a ride to four animals that help her escape from a dragon.

7

JULIA DONALDSON · AXEL SCHEFFLER

Charlie Cook's Favourite Book

By the creators of The Gruffalo

g   Someone very large gets new clothes and helps others with their problems.

8

JULIA DONALDSON · AXEL SCHEFFLER

THE GRUFFALO'S CHILD

h   A very big animal helps an adventurous small animal, who later repays the favour.

Answers on page 61!

7

Have You Ever Seen . . . ?

Who's afraid of Mouse?
Join the dots to find out!

Who Lives Where?

These animals all live in different places. Draw a line from each animal to its home: do you think it might live in the tree, in the stream, or in the logpile?

Answers on page 61!

Day and Night

Some animals are awake in the daytime, while others only like to come out at night. Decide if these animals are day or night creatures – or both!

Bats

Bats are small furry flying mammals (which mean they don't lay eggs, but have babies). Bats sleep upside down during the day.

Day ◯ Night ◯ Both ◯

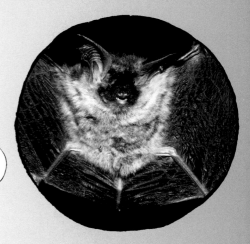

Foxes

Foxes live everywhere – in the countryside, but also in towns and cities. They eat almost everything, including berries, worms, spiders and leftover pizza! They tend to hide away in the daytime.

Day ◯ Night ◯ Both ◯

Frogs

Frogs live in or near water, where they lay their eggs. They eat insects and worms, which are easier to catch in the dark.

Day ◯ Night ◯ Both ◯

Owls

Owls have large eyes and can fly very quietly, which helps them to catch mice and insects when they hunt in darkness. They normally live alone and sleep during the day.

Day Night ⬤ Both ⬤

Squirrels

Tree squirrels have bushy tails, large teeth and special paws that mean they can climb down trees head-first. They eat mainly nuts, seeds and berries and they sleep in trees at night.

Day Night Both

Snakes

Snakes are cold-blooded, so they need the right temperature to move and feed. If it gets too hot or cold they have to rest. In cooler countries this means they need sunlight; in hot countries they will be happier after sunset.

Day ⬤ Night 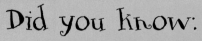 Both ⬤

Did you know:

Animals that are active at night are called **nocturnal**. Animals that come out in the daytime are called **diurnal**. Animals that prefer dusk and dawn, between day and night, are called **crepuscular**.

11

A Year of Activities: What Can You Spot?

Whatever the time of year, there's always something interesting to see outside. If you see any of these, tick the box!

Flowers

Even in winter, there are some flowers about if you look carefully.

Snowdrops flower very early in the year.

Crocuses are bright and colourful.

Hellebores can flower all winter.

Leaves

Some trees and bushes keep their leaves all year; others lose their leaves in the winter.

Tree **blossom**: this is a winter-flowering cherry tree.

New leaf **buds**

Holly **leaf**

Did you know:

Evergreen trees keep their leaves all year. Trees that lose their leaves in winter are **deciduous**.

Birds

Some birds stay all year, while others fly away for the winter. This is called **migration**.

The **robin** doesn't mind the cold.

Geese **migrate** for the winter.

Animals

Some animals sleep all winter and wake up in the spring. This is called **hibernation**.

Squirrels can be seen at any time of year.

Hedgehogs hibernate in the colder months.

Ladybirds and insects hibernate in the winter.

13

A Giant's Walk

George has been for a walk. Can you follow his path and complete the challenges on the way?

START HERE!

1. What kind of pattern can you see on a giraffe's skin?

   a. Stripes ☐

   b. Patches ☐

   c. Spots ☐

2. Which of these three flags is the same as the one on the goat's boat?

   a. ☐

   b. ☐

   c. ☐

Answers on page 61!

6. That's the end of George's new clothes, but he doesn't mind. Add some more patches to George's comfy old gown.

6

5

5. Dogs can howl, growl, whimper and bark. **Can you?**

4. How many mice are looking for a new home?

4

3. Draw a pattern on Fox's new 'sleeping bag'!

3

15

Who Gets What?

George gives away his new clothes to help his friends, but who gets what? Tick the right piece of clothing each time.

This chilly giraffe has a long cold neck. What does George give her to keep warm?

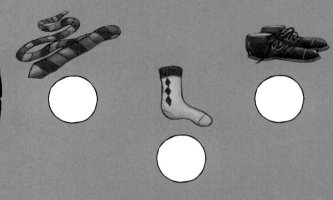

The dog keeps getting stuck in the mud! What does George give him to make a new path across the bog?

Answers on page 61!

3

Fox dropped his sleeping bag in a puddle! What does George give him to sleep in?

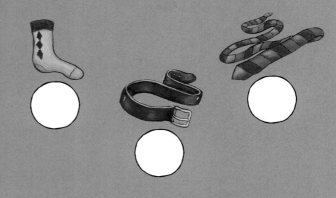

Goat's sail blew away in a storm. What does George replace it with?

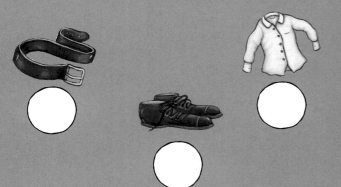

4

5

This poor little mouse lost her house in a fire. What does George use for her new home?

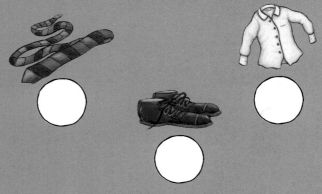

A House for a Mouse

Oh dear!
This little mouse house has burnt down.
Can you draw a new one for the tiny family?

A Letter for George

George got a lovely note from everyone he helped —
but some letters are missing. Can you fill them in?

Your tie is a scar....
for a cold giraffe,
Your shirt's on a boa....
as a ....ail for a goat,
Your shoe is a house
for a little white ....ouse,
One of your ....ocks
is a bed for a fox,
Your belt helped a ....og, who was
crossing a bog,
So here is a very
fine crow....
to go with the sandals and gown
of the KINDEST giant in town.

Water Colours

It's time to dig out your paints or pencils and follow the key to colour this picture – try not to go over the lines!

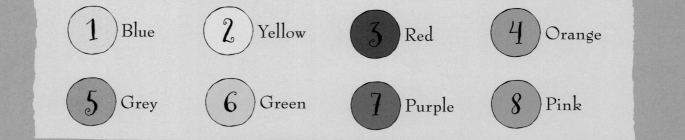

1 Blue	**2** Yellow	**3** Red	**4** Orange
5 Grey	**6** Green	**7** Purple	**8** Pink

Creature Pattern Match

Draw what you think comes next in each pattern.

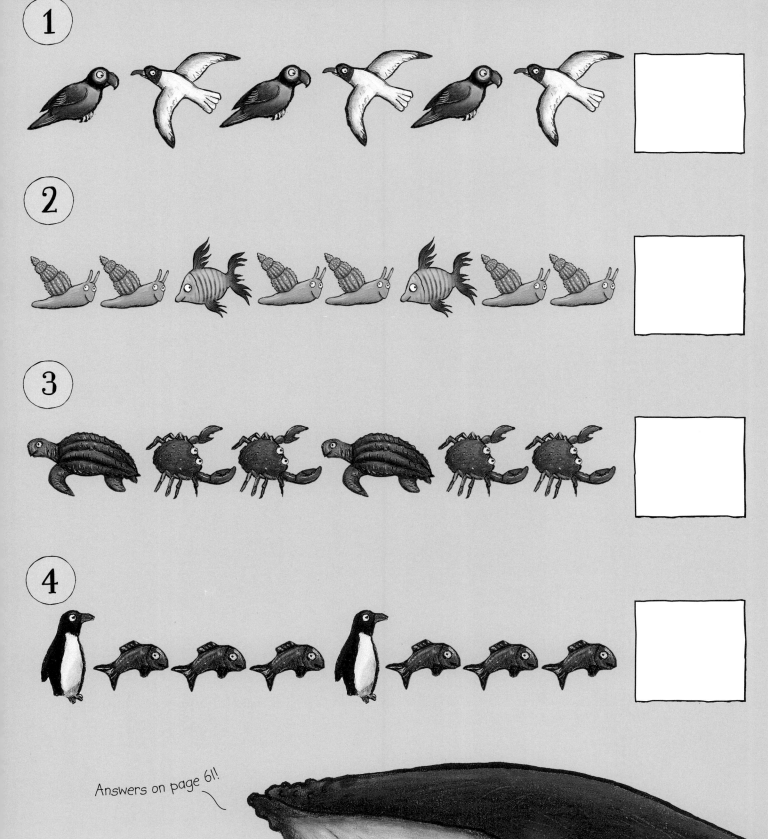

Answers on page 61!

So Many Boats!

There's a lot to see in this busy harbour. Count how many seagulls, snails, cats, and boats there are, and write the numbers in the boxes.

Seagulls

Snails

Boats

Answers on page 61!

Cats

ASK A GROWN-UP FOR HELP

A Year of Activities: Outdoor Fun

When you get the chance, go outside and do something.
The weather doesn't have to be warm and sunny (though it helps!).

Go Crabbing

Shops near the coast sell special crabbing lines, with a bag to hold bait instead of a sharp hook. Crabs are fond of raw bacon! You will also need a small bucket of seawater to keep your catch in.

Find a safe, quiet place to dangle your bait in the water. When you feel a tug on the line, pull it up gently.

If there is a greedy crab nibbling on your bait, pick it off (hold it across the back, between thumb and forefinger) and pop it in your bucket.

You may only catch one or two crabs, or be lucky and catch lots!

When you finish, tip your bucket out gently to release the crabs back into the water.

Did you know:

There are places where you can spot wild seals, dolphins or even whales, often without even leaving the shore.

Build a Sandcastle

If you can get to a sandy beach, you MUST build a sandcastle! (You don't even have to be on the beach, if you can find a big sandpit.) You can just use your hands, or a spade if you have one. Will it be round or square? Big enough to sit inside, or tall enough to stand on? Will it have towers, a moat, a bridge?

If the sand is fine, you can scoop up handfuls of very watery sand and dribble it on to your castle to make fantastic turrets and spikes.

Use shells, seaweed, pebbles or sea glass to decorate your castle.

Make a Mandala

This challenge works well at a beach, in the park or in a wood. Gather your materials first: you could use pebbles, stones, shells, driftwood, pinecones, nuts, feathers or seaweed.

Arrange the objects in neat rings, spreading out from the centre. Take a picture before the wind or tide moves your art.

It's a Squash and a Squeeze!

How many creatures can YOU fit in the little old lady's house?
Draw as many different animals as you can, without
them overlapping!

Whose Shadow?

Help the little old lady work out who's who by drawing
a line from each animal to its shadow.

1

2

3

4

a

b

c

d

Answers on page 61!

Magnificent Masks

Make these marvellous masks and you can act out
your own version of *A Squash and a Squeeze*!

You will need:

- Tracing paper
- Thin white card or stiff paper
- Safety scissors
- Coloured pens/pencils/paints
- Thin elastic, or a large rubber band cut into a strip
- Stapler or tape
- A grown-up helper

How to make a mask

1. Trace over a mask outline in pencil. You can find the outlines on pages 30 and 31.

2. Turn the tracing over, place it on the card and draw over the back of your tracing. This will transfer a pencil line to the card.

3. Cut out the mask. Ask your adult helper to cut out the eyeholes.

28

4. Fold along the dotted line to make the nose (and the ears on the pig).

6. Tape or staple one end of the elastic (or rubber band) to one side of the mask. Ask a grown-up to help with the stapler. Check how the mask fits on your head before fixing the other end of the elastic.

5. Colour in the mask with pens, pencils or paint and leave it to dry.

Animal Masks

Templates for masks

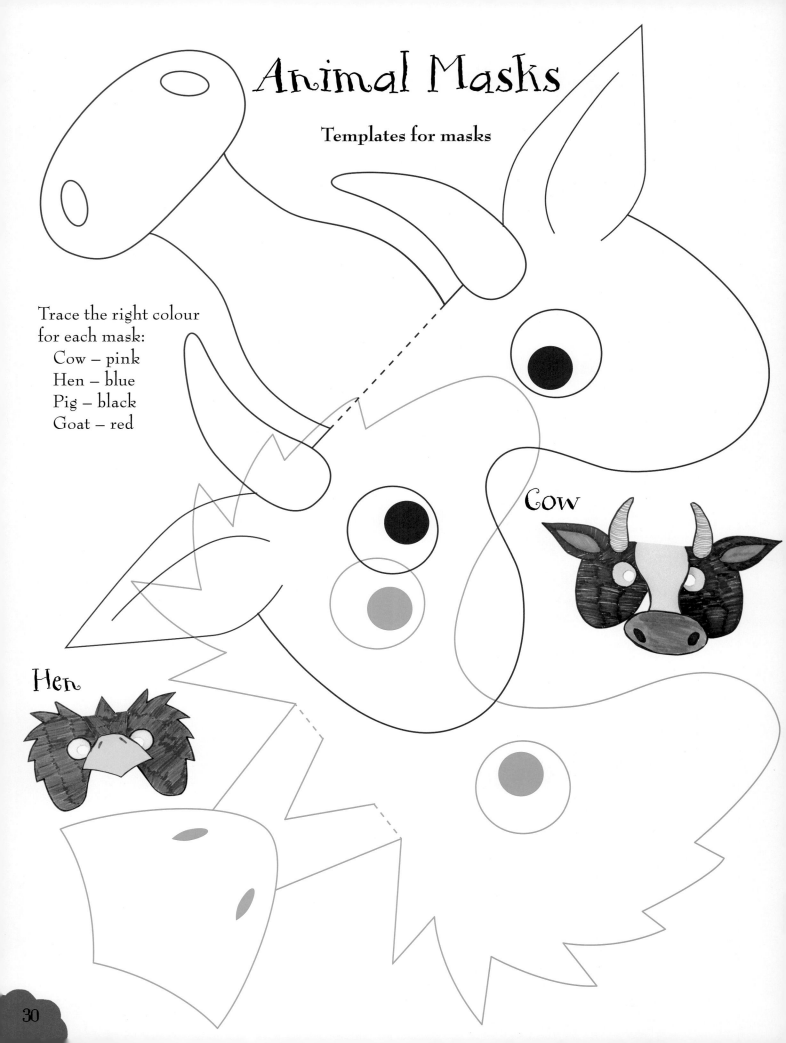

Trace the right colour
for each mask:
Cow – pink
Hen – blue
Pig – black
Goat – red

Cow

Hen

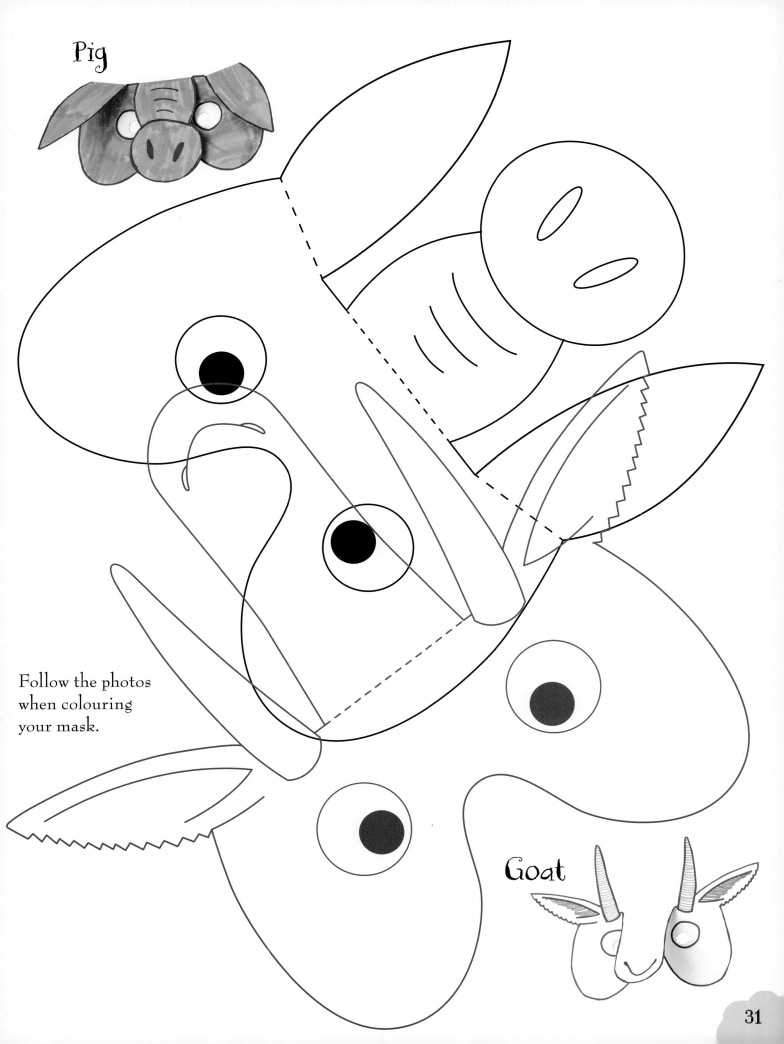

Pig

Follow the photos when colouring your mask.

Goat

31

Magic Mirth

Cackle and smile at these
wickedly funny witchy jokes!

How do you make
a witch itch?

**Take away
her W!**

How does a witch
tell the time?

**She looks at her
witch-watch!**

Why won't a witch
wear a bobble hat?

**There's no
point.**

What does the
witch put on her
plait?

Scare-spray!

What do witches
race on?

Vroomsticks!

Why did the
witch fly over
the swamp?

**Because she
couldn't fly
under it.**

What has six
legs and flies?

**The witch on her
broomstick –
with her cat!**

What was the
name of the pot
used for making
spells?

**It was called-
Ron.**

Why did the old
witch have stiff
joints?

**She had
broomatism!**

Odd Witch Out

These witches all look the same
but one is different from the others!
Can you find her?

Answers on page 61!

33

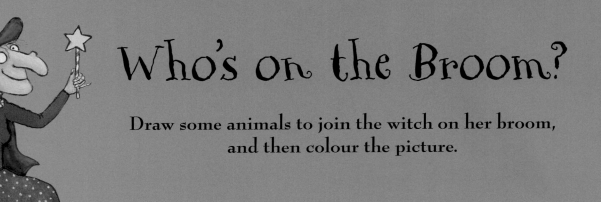

Who's on the Broom?

Draw some animals to join the witch on her broom,
and then colour the picture.

Answers on page 61!

Dancing Differences

Everybody is happy now the dragon has flown away!
Can you spot the eight differences between these two pictures?

35

Spells and Potions

The witch is mixing up a potion in her cauldron.
Draw some interesting ingredients to add to it,
then give your spell a name.

Wish for a Wand

You need an impressive wand to make your spells
and potions with!

ASK A GROWN-UP FOR HELP

You will need:

- A long thin bendy stick about 1m long – willow is ideal
- A ruler
- Coloured string or thread
- Decorations: feathers, beads, twigs, pine cones, pipe cleaners – whatever you can find!

How to make it

1. Bend the stick 15cm from the end – don't snap it!

2. Bend it again (in the same direction) three more times at 10cm intervals, overlapping the end as you go.

3. Arrange the folded parts into a star shape, and then tie the end to the main handle.

4. Decorate your wand. You could thread beads on coloured string and tie them in a loop just below the star. Why not wind coloured pipe cleaners around the handle, or tie bunches of feathers or twigs to it?

A Year of Activities: Weather Watching

A storm can strike at any time of year. Learn the signs of approaching rain so your day isn't spoiled – and if it is raining, make a rainstick so you can join in!

Is it going to rain?

If there are lots of fluffy white clouds moving overhead, it probably won't rain. These are called **cumulus** clouds.

But if you see a bigger, taller cloud coming towards you . . . with dark patches . . . then watch out! If the wind changes direction as the cloud comes towards you and you feel it get colder, then yes, it's probably going to rain. That's called a **cumulonimbus** cloud.

Finally, if you see low, grey clouds covering the whole sky . . . it's probably already raining! These are called **nimbostratus** clouds.

Make a Rainstick

ASK A GROWN-UP FOR HELP

You will need:

- The tube from a kitchen towel roll
- Aluminum foil
- A handful of dried beans
- Sticky tape
- Stickers, coloured rubber bands or string to decorate your rainstick

How to make it

1. Scrunch up some foil to the same length as your tube. Place it in the tube.

2. Place a piece of foil over one end of the tube. Hold it in place with tape.

3. Place the dried beans in the tube and seal the other end in the same way. Now decorate your rainstick.

Who's Hiding in the Rainforest?

Monkey has lost his mum! Can you find her hidden
in the rainforest? Who else is hiding?
Tick them off the list when you find them.

Answers on page 61!

41

Where is Monkey's Mum?

Answer on page 61!

Which of these tangled vines leads to Monkey's mum?

1

2

3

Parrot Portrait

Can you copy this picture of Parrot into the blank grid below?
Work on one square at a time, then colour it in!

Six Monkeys' Morris

This is a simple version of a game that has been played for hundreds of years. Play it with a friend, your mum or your pet monkey.

You will need:

- An opponent
- Six counters each – you could use coins or buttons. Each player needs a different type of counter so you can see whose is whose.
- This book!

How to win

When you place three counters in a line, you can remove one of your opponent's counters. When they only have two counters left on the board, you win!

How to play

1) Take it in turns to put a counter on the board, on one of the flowers.
2) Whenever one of you has three counters in a line, take an opponent's counter off the board (it can't be used again).
3) When you have both placed all your counters, take it in turns to slide a counter along a line to an empty flower. If this move completes a line of three, remove one of your opponent's counters.
4) When one player only has three counters left (and is about to lose), they don't have to slide their counters, they can 'fly' them to any empty flower. This gives them a last chance to fight back!

Make Up a Story

Charlie Cook loves a story with lots of twists and changes.
Can you make up your own tale using these interesting
characters? Or you could add your own!

Once upon a time, a _____

met a _____ .

"Hello," said the _____

"Shall we go and _____ ?"

So they went to _____ where

a _____ was _____ .

Suddenly a huge _____ appeared.

"Oh no!" yelled the _____. "It's going

to _____!" Luckily that didn't

happen, because _____

_____ .

And they all _____ instead.

Now you need a book to put your story in!

47

Make Your Own Books

These little books are quick and easy to make —
perfect for writing or drawing your own stories.

You will need:

- A sheet of A4 paper
- Safety scissors
- Pens or pencils
- An adult helper

How to make a book

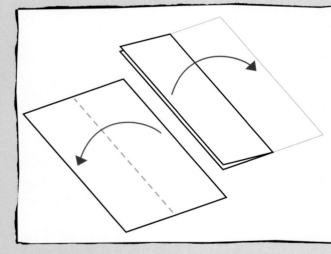

1. Fold the paper in half lengthways, make
   a good crease, then unfold the paper.

2. Fold the paper in half away from you,
   so the centre fold is nearest.

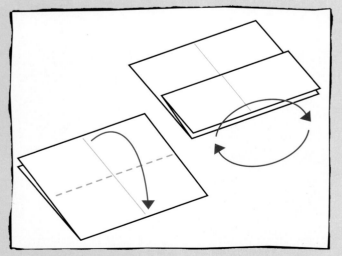

3. Fold the top edge down to the centre
   fold. Turn the whole thing over.

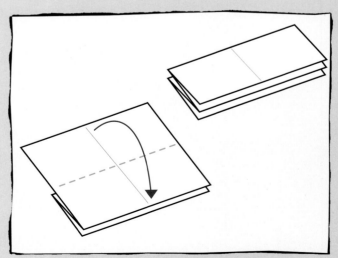

4. Fold the top edge down to the centre
   fold on the other side.

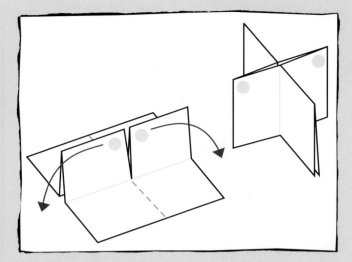

5. Unfold the paper so the centre fold sticks up. Cut down the crease you made in step 1.

6. Hold the paper on either side of this cut and bend it sideways.

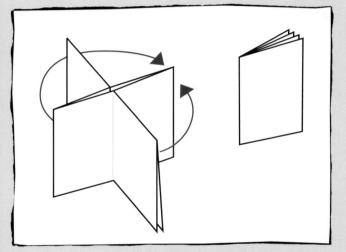

7. Press the book flat, then fold it in half.

8. You could start a story right away, but why not add a stiff cover? Fold a piece of card and cut it slightly larger than your book. Then stick just the back page of your book inside.

9. Decorate your book to suit your story. Glue foil to the cover for a book about robots. Stick on cotton wool for a wintery tale. The decoration could even inspire your stories!

Look for a Book

Hidden in this grid are lots of the characters that
Charlie Cook reads about. Can you spot them all?
Words run forwards, down and even diagonally!

~~Pirate~~
Parrot
Bear
Goldilocks
Knight
Dragon
Frog
Book
Owl
Rook
Thief
King
Crocodile
Queen
Astronaut
Ghost

A	G	N	T	H	I	E	F	G	A
S	B	H	G	B	R	F	R	O	G
T	C	R	O	C	O	D	I	L	E
R	Q	P	E	S	J	O	L	D	K
O	U	E	I	A	T	N	K	I	N
N	E	P	A	R	R	O	T	L	I
A	E	R	B	K	A	O	M	O	G
U	N	C	E	R	I	T	O	C	H
T	D	R	A	G	O	N	E	K	T
W	E	F	R	O	W	L	G	S	U

Answers on page 61!

51

A Year of Activities: Helping Wildlife

Whether you've got a big garden or just a window box, you can do something to help wild birds and insects. There are things you can do all year, but birds need special help in the winter when food is scarce.

Planting for birds and insects

These are all good food for insects or birds at different times of the year. Some can even be planted in a pot. Why not try growing some?

Sunflower

Honeysuckle

Buddleia

Lavender

Crabapple

Barberry

Sloe

Holly

Watch out for spikes!

Make a Fat Ball

Once winter sets in, birds need extra food. A fat ball will attract them to your garden.

ASK A GROWN-UP FOR HELP

You will need:

- Four disposable cups
- A pencil
- String
- Four small twigs or buttons
- Bird seed, raisins, peanuts and grated cheese – about a handful of each
- Lard – about two handfuls
- An adult helper

1. Ask a grown-up to help you poke a hole in the bottom of the cups with a pencil. Thread string through the holes, and tie a firm knot around a small twig or button (to keep the fat ball on the string).

2. Allow the lard to warm to room temperature, then use a butter knife to cut it into small pieces and put in a large mixing bowl.

4. Pack the sticky mix in each cup. Put the cups in the fridge to set for an hour.

3. Add the other ingredients, and squidge it with your fingers until the fat sticks it all together.

5. Hold the cups upside down and tap the base to remove the fat balls. Then tie them up outside where you can watch the action!

53

Snowy Maze

Help the Gruffalo's Child get away from the Big
Bad Mouse and back to the safety of the cave!

Answers on page 61!

It's Time for a Feast!

Here's some fantastic food fit for a hungry Gruffalo,
though maybe not for a MIDNIGHT feast –
even the Gruffalo's Child needs her sleep.

Gruffalo cakes

You will need:

for 12 fairy cakes

- 125g unsalted butter, softened
- 125g golden caster sugar
- 100g self-raising white flour
- 25g cocoa powder
- 1 teaspoon baking powder
- 2 eggs, beaten
- An adult helper

for the icing

- 60g unsalted butter
- 30g cocoa powder
- 250g icing sugar
- 3 tablespoons milk

for the decoration

- Chocolate buttons
- Orange and green sweets
- Mini marshmallows

1. Ask a grown-up to preheat the oven to 200°C/fan 190°C/Gas 6. Line a fairy cake tin with 12 paper cases.

2. Using a electric whisk or spoon, cream together the butter and sugar. Add the beaten eggs a little at a time and whisk.

3. Sift the flour, cocoa and baking powder into the mixture a little at a time, folding it in with a spoon.

6. When the cupcakes are completely cold, spread the icing on with a butter knife.

4. Divide the mixture equally between the paper cases (about two-thirds full). Ask a grown-up to bake your cakes for 15-20 minutes until the cakes are springy to the touch. Leave to cool.

7. Decorate the cupcakes to make Gruffalo faces. Use chocolate buttons for ears; orange and green sweets for the eyes and nose; and mini marshmallows for the teeth and horns. You can ask a grown-up to cut them for you, or use safety scissors.

5. To make the icing, ask a grown-up to melt the butter in a bowl in a microwave. Sift in the cocoa powder, and then stir in the icing sugar a little at a time. Add a little milk to make the icing spreadable.

ASK A GROWN-UP FOR HELP

Cheesy Moon Biscuits

You will need:

- 120g plain flour
- 120g margarine
- 120g mature cheddar cheese, grated
- An adult helper

How to make

1. Ask an adult to preheat the oven to 170°C/fan 150°C/Gas 5.

2. Mix all the ingredients together in a bowl using your (clean) hands until it makes a dough.

4. Place the biscuits on a floured baking tray and ask a grown-up to bake them for 10-15 minutes until they are golden and crispy.

3. Roll out the dough until it's about 5mm thick. Use a round cutter to make full moon biscuits. You could also use moon and star cutters.

Gruffalo Tea

You will need:

- 4 fruit tea bags
- ice cubes
- sparkling water
- a selection of berries – raspberries, blueberries, strawberries
- An adult helper

ASK A GROWN-UP FOR HELP

How to make

1. Put the tea bags in a heatproof jug. Ask an adult to add boiling water and leave to cool.

2. When the fruit tea is cool, put plenty of ice in a glass and half-fill with fruit tea. Top up with sparkling water.

3. Add a handful of berries to each glass.

Sweet Dreams

The Gruffalo's Child is sleeping deeply. But what might she be dreaming of? Will you draw something fun, or scary?

Answers

Page 6: Have You Read . . . ?
1: b, 2: g, 3: e, 4: f, 5: h, 6: c, 7: a, 8: d.

Page 9: Who Lives Where?
Owl and Squirrel live in the tree, Frog and Fish live in the stream; Snake lives in the logpile.

Page 10: Day and Night
Bats: night, Foxes: night, Frogs: night, Owls: night, Squirrels: day, Snakes: day and night.

Page 14: A Giant's Walk
1: b – Patches, 2: a, 4: 8

Page 16: Who Gets What?
1. Giraffe: tie, 2. Dog: belt, 3. Fox: sock, 4. Goat: shirt, 5. Mouse: shoe.

Page 19: A Letter for George
Your tie is a scarF for a cold giraffe,
Your shirt's on a boaT as a Sail for a goat.
Your shoe is a house for a little white Mouse.
One of your Socks is a bed for a fox.
Your belt helped a Dog who was crossing a bog.
So here is a very fine crowN, to go with the sandals and gown of the KINDEST giant in town.

Page 21: Creature Pattern Match
1: Red bird, 2: Fish, 3: Turtle, 4: Penguin.

Page 22: So Many Boats!
Seagulls: 8, Snails: 10, Boats: 6, Cat: 1.

Page 27: Whose Shadow?
1: c, 2: d, 3: a, 4: b.

Page 33: Odd Witch Out
4 is missing her wart on her nose.

Page 35: Dancing Differences

Page 40: Who's Hiding in the Rainforest?

Page 42: Where is Monkey's Mum?
Line 1 leads to Monkey's mum.

Page 50: Look for a Book

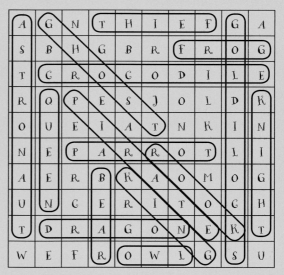

Page 54: Snowy Maze